The Kangaroo Pouch

A story
about surrogacy
for young children

By Sarah Phillips Pellet

illustrated by Laurie A. Faust

Forward by Gail Taylor, Founder of Growing
Generations and Fertility Futures, LLC

Order this book online at www.trafford.com/06-2315
or email orders@trafford.com

Most Trafford titles are also available at major online book retailers.

Note for Librarians: A cataloguing record for this book is available from Library
and Archives Canada at www.collectionscanada.ca/amicus/index-e.html

Printed in Victoria, BC, Canada.

ISBN: 978-1-4251-0557-0

*We at Trafford believe that it is the responsibility of us all, as both individuals
and corporations, to make choices that are environmentally and socially sound.
You, in turn, are supporting this responsible conduct each time you purchase a
Trafford book, or make use of our publishing services. To find out how you are
helping, please visit www.trafford.com/responsiblepublishing.html*

*Our mission is to efficiently provide the world's finest, most comprehensive
book publishing service, enabling every author to experience success.
To find out how to publish your book, your way, and have it available
worldwide, visit us online at www.trafford.com/10510*

www.trafford.com

North America & international
toll-free: 1 888 232 4444 (USA & Canada)
phone: 250 383 6864 ♦ fax: 250 383 6804
email: info@trafford.com

The United Kingdom & Europe
phone: +44 (0)1865 722 113 ♦ local rate: 0845 230 9601
facsimile: +44 (0)1865 722 868 ♦ email: info.uk@trafford.com

10 9 8 7 6 5 4

For Matthew and Jonathan
Joshua and Jacob

The Kangaroo Pouch is a touching children's story of how one happy family can help to create another. This tale of a family created through surrogacy is a brilliant, clear understanding of what is sometimes a complex conversation for adults to share with a child.

The Kangaroo Pouch is a simple and special book that all families touched by the surrogacy process will love reading with their children. Sarah has an exciting and genuine approach in telling the story through the eyes of a surrogate's child. Surrogacy is a rewarding experience for all who participate in creating families through this special journey.

This book is a valuable resource for every family and I am thrilled to share **The Kangaroo Pouch** with all people involved with the surrogacy process.

Gail Taylor
President and Founder of Growing
Generations and Fertility Futures Int'l LLC

Hello, my name is Oliver. I am a very lucky kangaroo. I live with my father, mother, and my big brother, Oscar. We are a happy family.

We live in a world where lots and lots of kangaroos have lots and lots of baby kangaroos.

But some kangaroos, like the Bouncing-Hopsalots, don't have any babies hopping around their home. This makes them very sad.

They love each other and would like to be able to have babies to love as well. That is how a family gets made – one of the first ingredients is love.

A baby gets made from two tiny things called cells. One cell comes from a man and the other cell comes from a woman. The cells are joined together to make a baby and then it grows in a pouch.

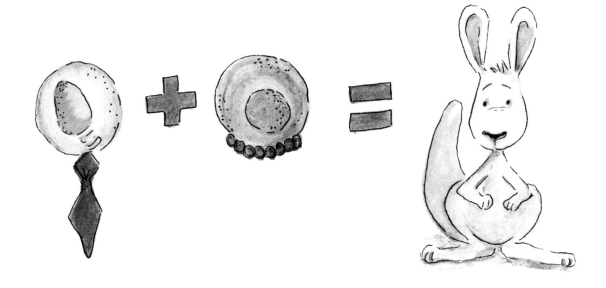

You see, pouches are where baby kangaroos are kept cozy and warm until they are ready to come out into the world.

One day, my mother
had an idea…

"I've already had my babies and we are really happy," she thought.

"And there are some kangaroos that can't have babies."

"What if I carry their baby
in my pouch?"
thought my mother.

"And when their baby is ready to come out into the world,
they can have it back!" she thought.

So my mother talked to the Bouncing-Hopsalots and they agreed that this would be a wonderful idea!

When the time was right, the Bouncing-Hopsalots gave my mother their teensy, weensy baby to put into her pouch.

And for several months afterwards, my mother kept their baby warm and cozy.

My family and I still did all of our usual things together like playing soccer, going on picnics, and riding our scooters in the park.

While the baby was growing in my mother's pouch, she played tapes of the Bouncing-Hopsalots' voices so that their new baby would know how her parents would sound when she was ready to come out into the world.

My brother Oscar and I told silly jokes and read stories out loud to the new baby.

Then one day, baby Jemima Bouncing-Hopsalot was ready to come out into the world! She was a lot bigger than when she went into my mother's pouch and she cried alot; but she was very cute.

My mother gave the Bouncing-Hopsalots their baby back to them. They were over the moon with happiness.

Our happy family went back to the way it was before.

THE END

About the Author

Sarah Phillips Pellet, originally hailing from Massachusetts and Maine, graduated with a degree in journalism from Rutgers University and has been a business writer throughout her career. When faced with the prospect of informing her own children about her decision to act as a compassionate gestational surrogate on behalf of their aunt and uncle, she decided that the best way to approach this complex subject was through the use of a children's book. **The Kangaroo Pouch** was designed to address the decision-making process of becoming a surrogate, as well as what to expect during and after the pregnancy. Ms. Phillips Pellet lives with her family in New Jersey.

About the Illustrator

Laurie A. Faust studied at Herron School of Art, in Indianapolis, Indiana and currently works as an illustrator, event designer, graphic designer and muralist. She lives in Noblesville, Indiana with her husband and children.

About Growing Generations and Fertility Futures International, LLC

Headquartered in Los Angeles, California, Growing Generations LLC and Fertility Futures International LLC are the premiere surrogacy and egg donation agencies helping to create families worldwide.

Growing Generations LLC and Fertility Futures LLC mission statement is *Lives Created – Worlds Changed*. They have assisted thousands of surrogates intended parents and egg donors since 1996.

Surrogacy and egg donation are an innovative approach to aiding those who seek the joys of parenthood. Surrogates, donors and their families give a unique contribution in the creation of children through assisted reproduction.

To learn more about surrogacy, artificial insemination or egg donation, please visit growinggenerations.com or fertilityfutures.com.